the
bean
abc

The Bean abc

by
Richard Fowler

MACMILLAN
CHILDREN'S BOOKS

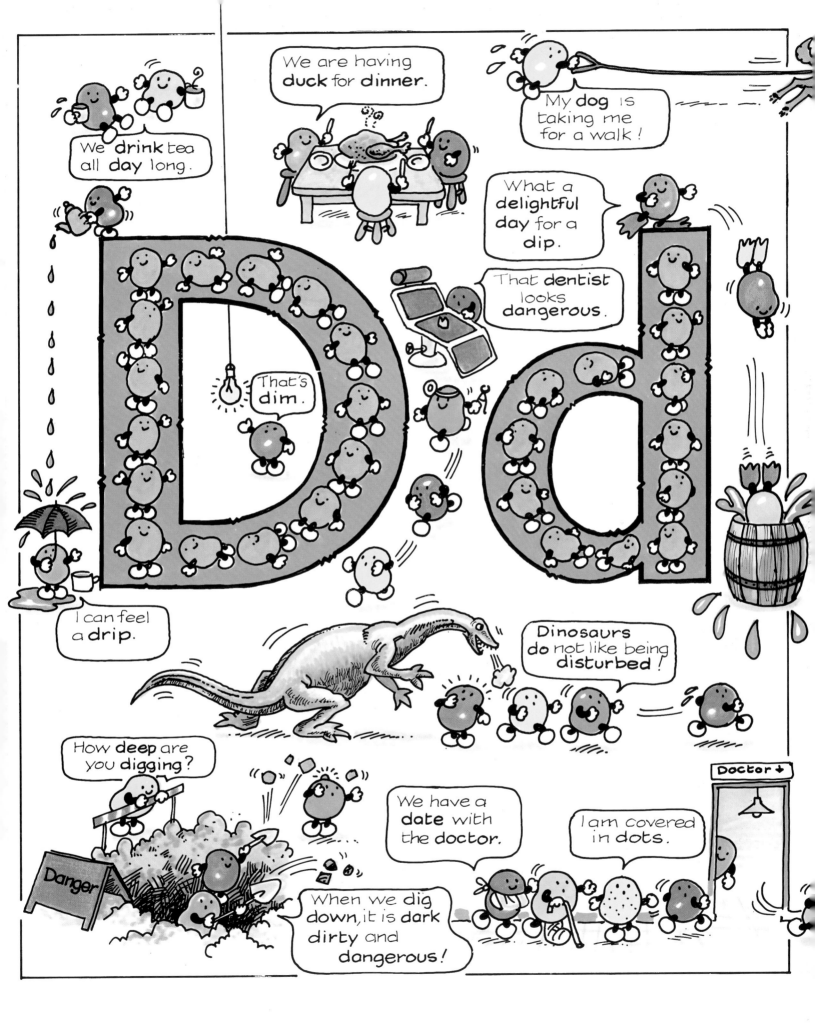

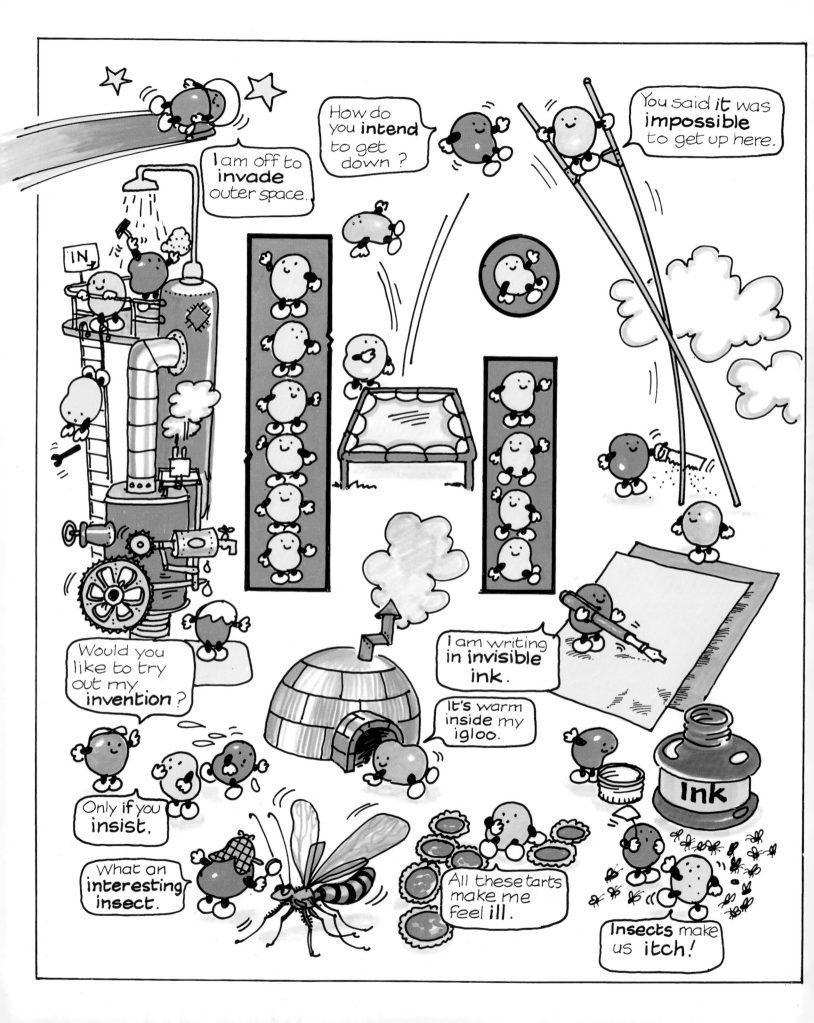

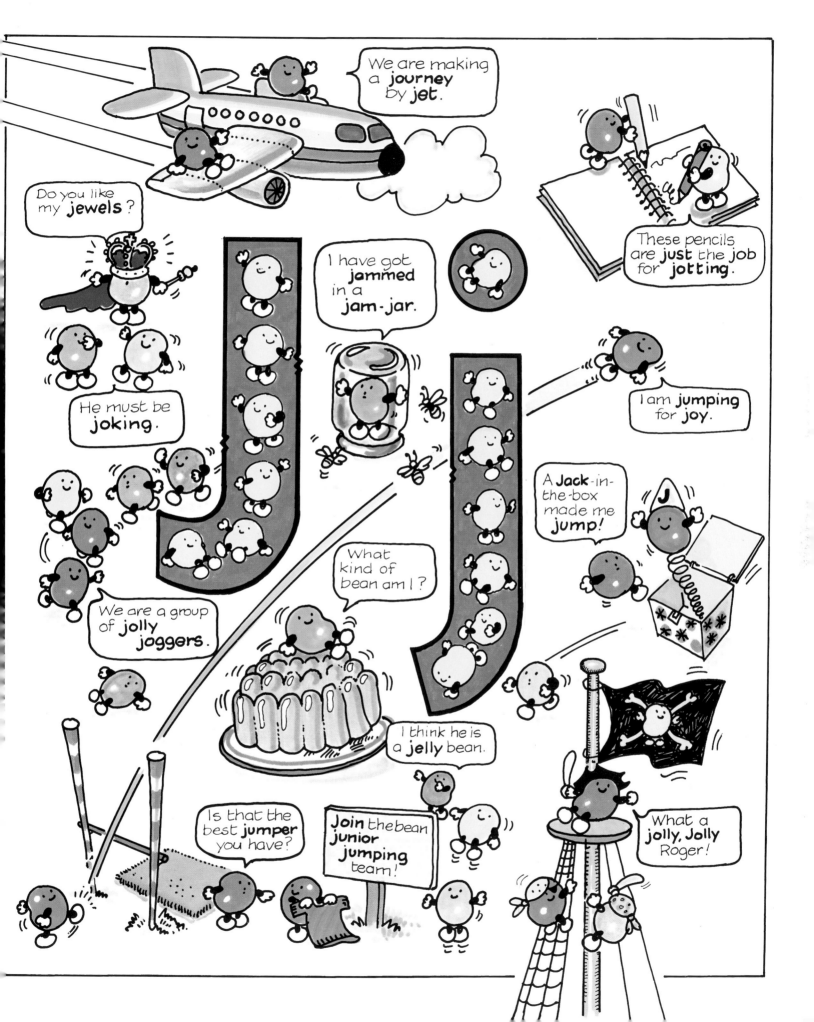

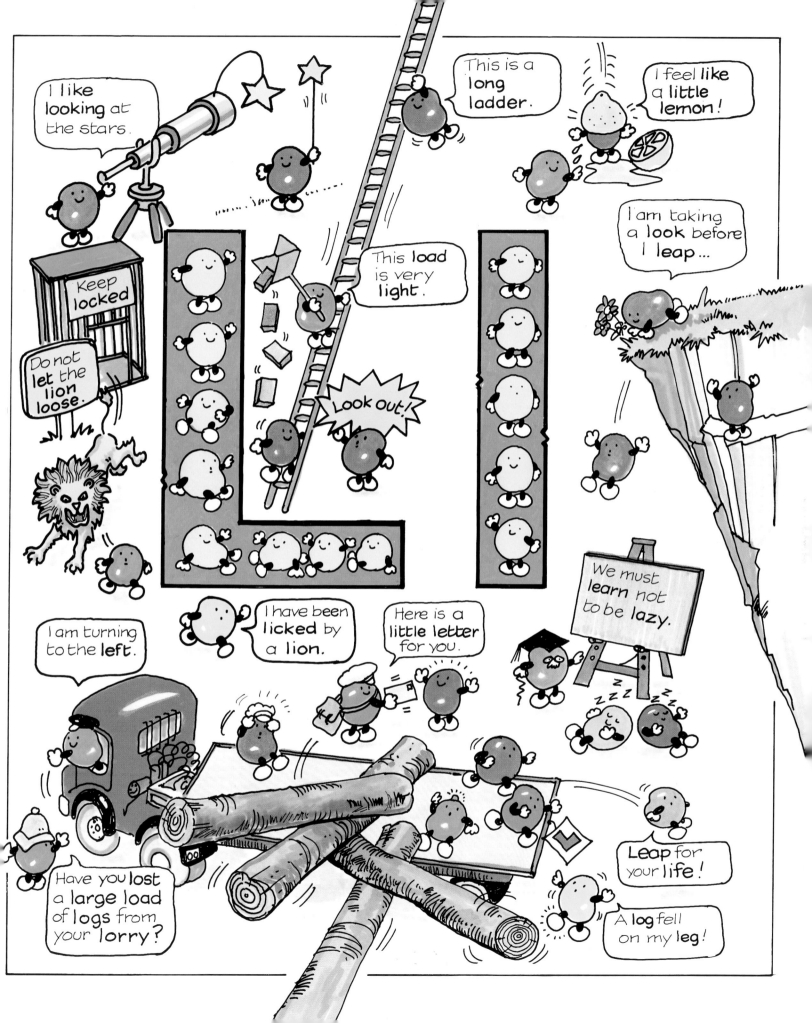

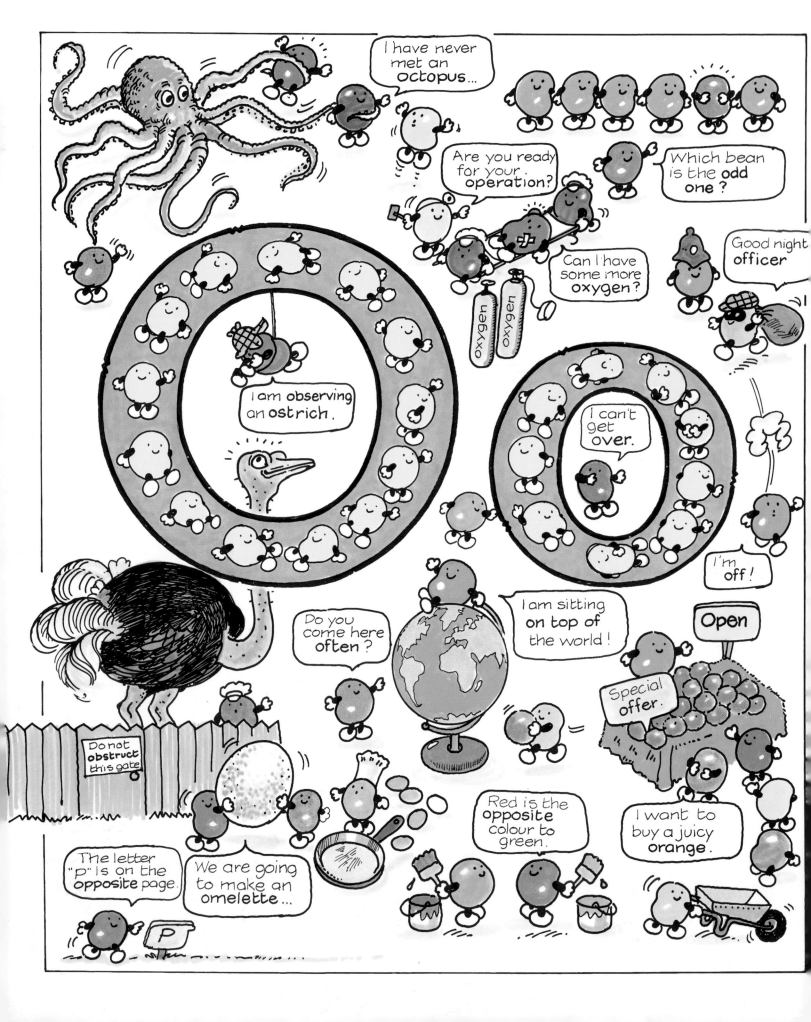

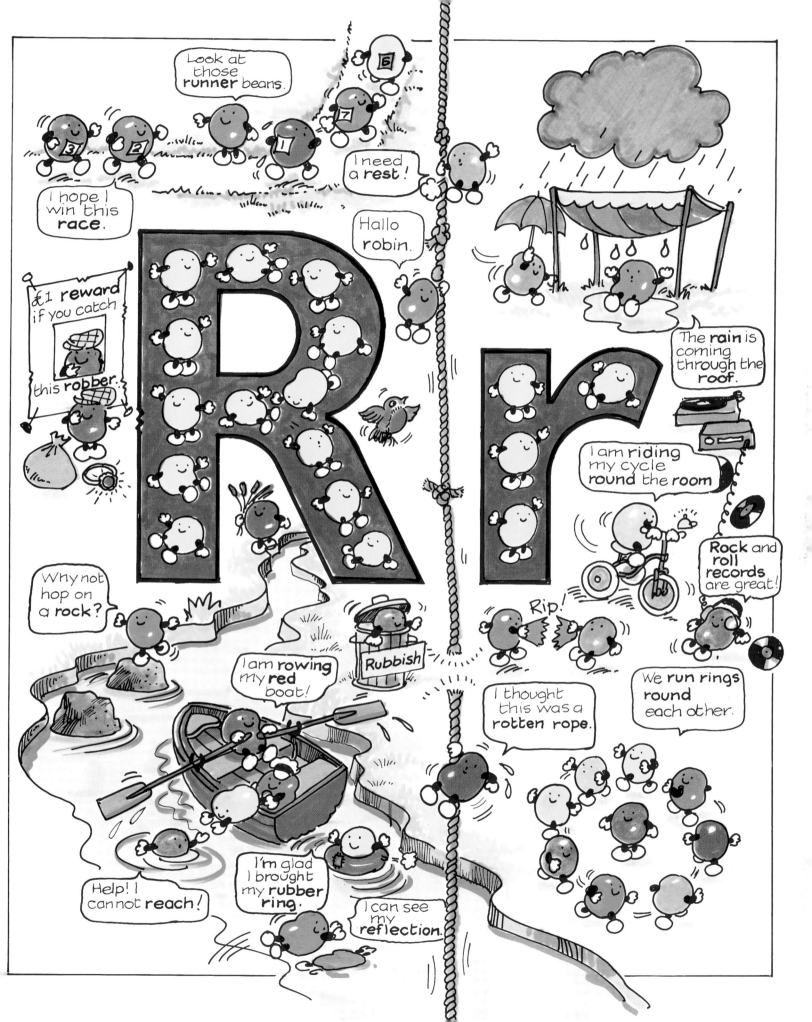

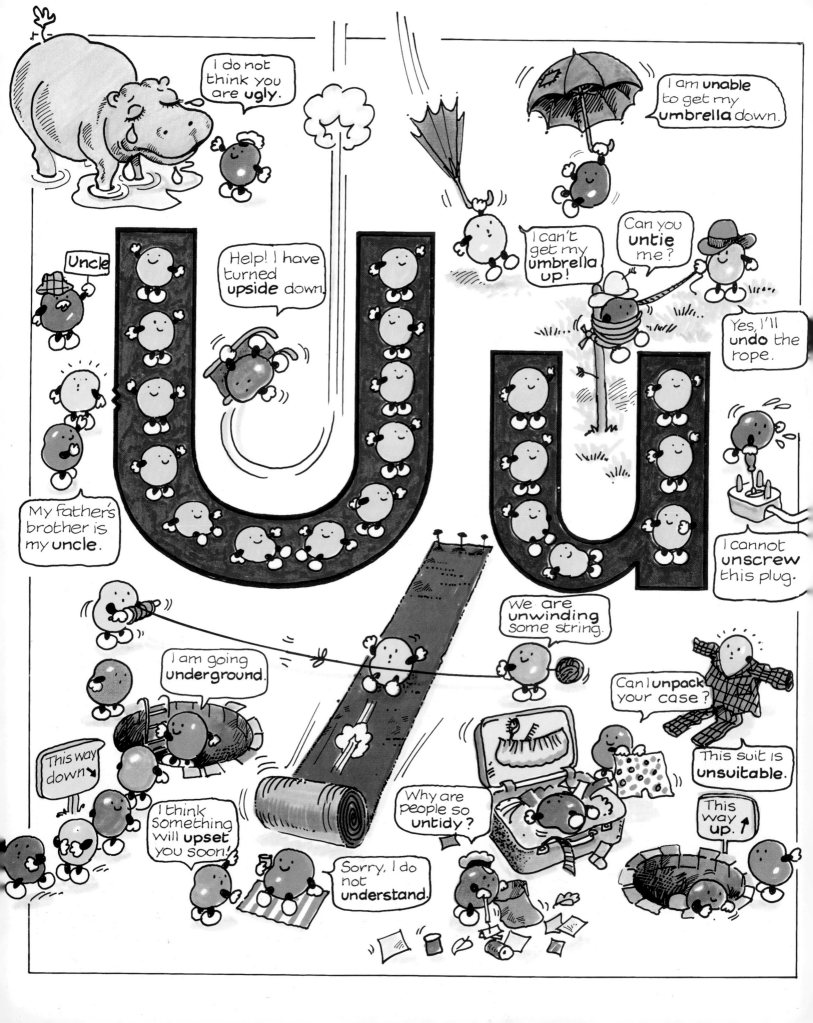

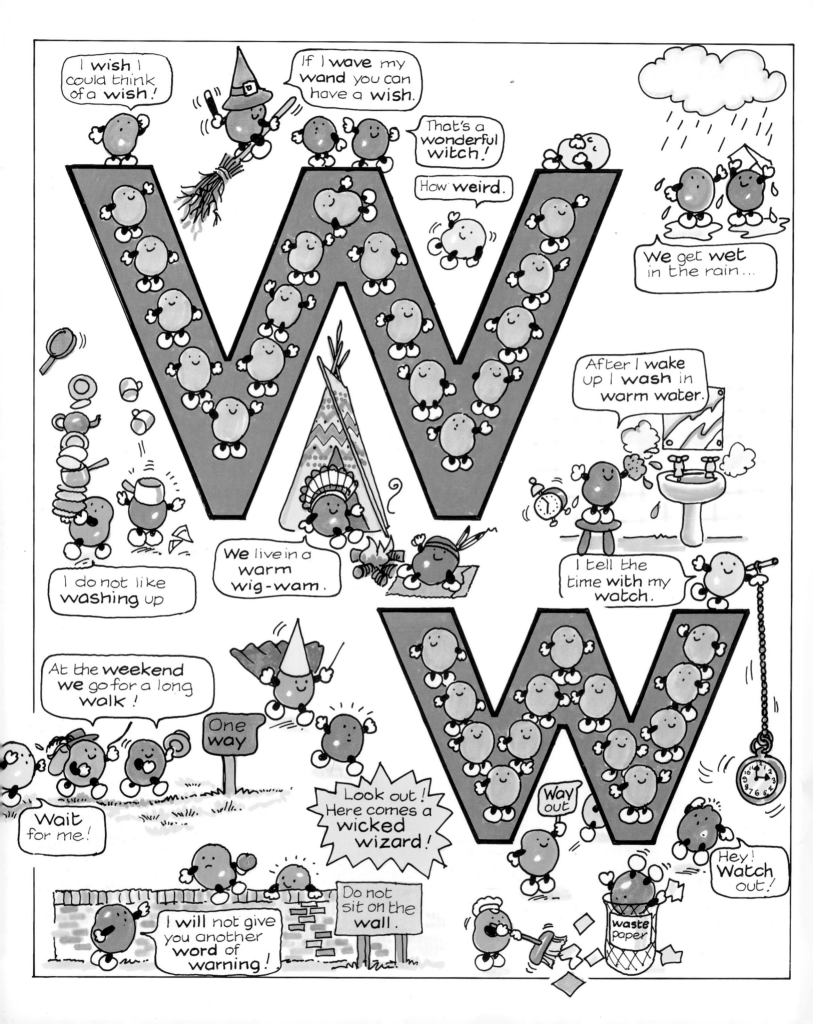

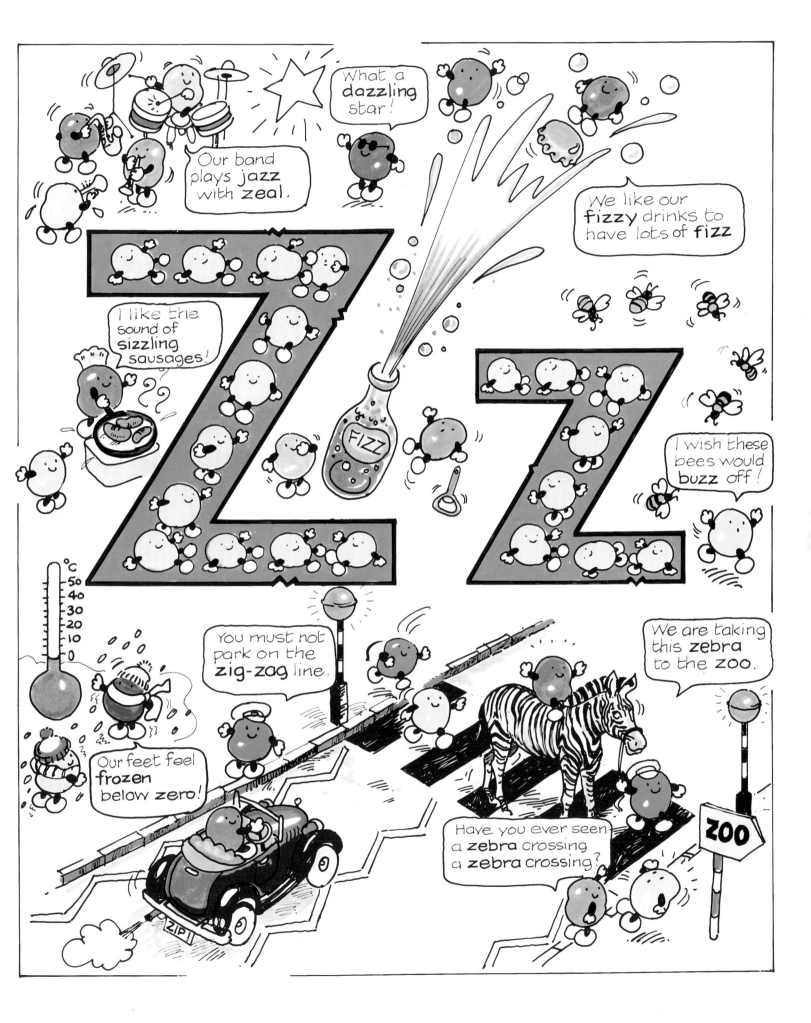

First published 1981 by Longman Group Limited
This edition published 1995 by Macmillan Children's Books
a division of Macmillan Publishers Limited
Cavaye Place London SW10 9PG and Basingstoke
Associated companies throughout the world

ISBN 0 333 63844 1

1 3 5 7 9 8 6 4 2

A CIP catalogue record for this book is available from the British Library
Printed in Hong Kong